The Red Pop Beads

by Violet Dutcher

The Red Pop Beads

Written by Violet Dutcher
Illustrated by Maren Tyedmers Hange

Library of Congress Number: 2020952874
International Standard Book Number: 978-1-60126-724-5

Masthof Press

219 Mill Road | Morgantown, PA 19543-9516
www.Masthof.com

The Red
Pop Beads

Every morning, two little Mennonite girls, Rhoda and Violet, put on a dress that their mother has sewn from fabric in plain colors. They do not wear shorts. They do not wear pants. They do not wear earrings or bracelets or necklaces.

DEDICATION

In loving memory of my sister,
Rhoda Mae, who died when
she was three years old, and I was six.

In loving tribute to my living sister,
Lois Diane, who wipes away
the tears. Always.

Lastly, and importantly,
to our grandchildren,
Austin, Allyson, and Rita.
You are gorgeous and ravishing.

She makes a bracelet and snaps it on her wrist. The red pop beads shine softly. "Violet," her mother says, "the bracelet is ravishing!" Violet looks at her mother and smiles.

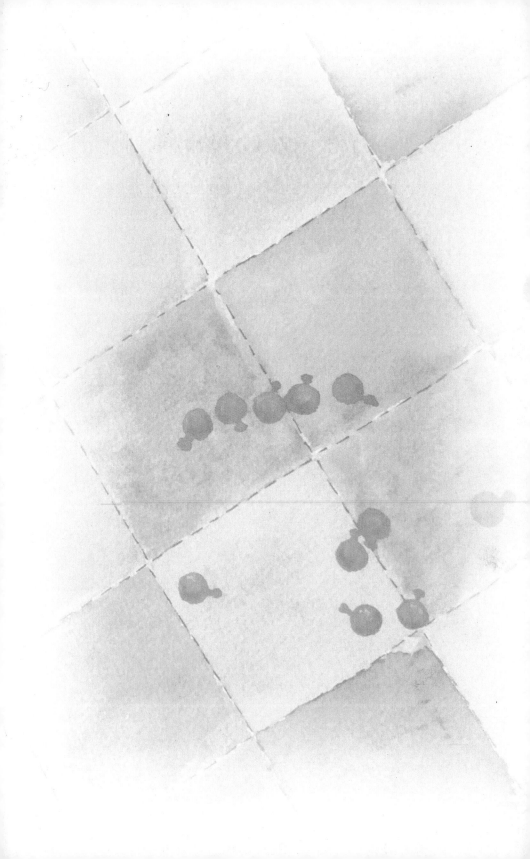

Sometimes, their mother adds lace to the collars on the dresses. Sometimes, she adds a sash to the dress and ties the sash in a large bow in the back. Rhoda and Violet like these dresses.

Every morning, Rhoda and Violet's mother combs their hair. The girls' hair is long, and their mother combs out all the tangles. Sometimes, when her hair is caught in the blue plastic comb, Violet says, "Ouch." Her mother combs her hair into two long braids with curls at the ends.

Then they run outside to play. The sun shines brightly. Red roses bloom along the white fence. The grass is green and soft. Dinger, the neighbor's dog, runs down to play with Violet and Rhoda.

One day, everything changed.

Rhoda is sick and does not get out of bed.

Violet's mother combs
and braids Violet's hair.

Violet does not go outside to play even though the sun shines brightly. Red roses bloom along the white fence. The grass is green and soft. Dinger, the neighbor's dog, runs down to play with Violet and Rhoda, but they are not outside.

Inside their house, Rhoda's room is dark and quiet. Rhoda is sick and stays in bed every day.

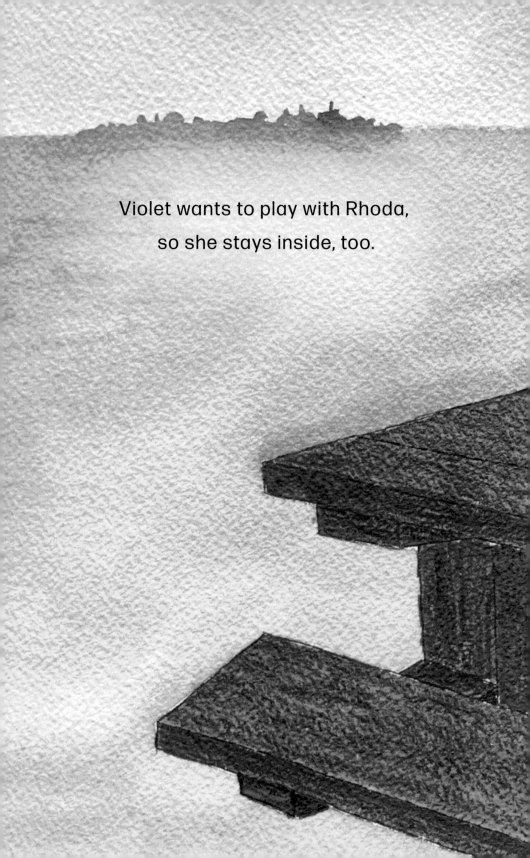

Violet wants to play with Rhoda,

so she stays inside, too.

One day, Aunt Martha and Uncle Mahlon come to visit. They bring Rhoda a present.

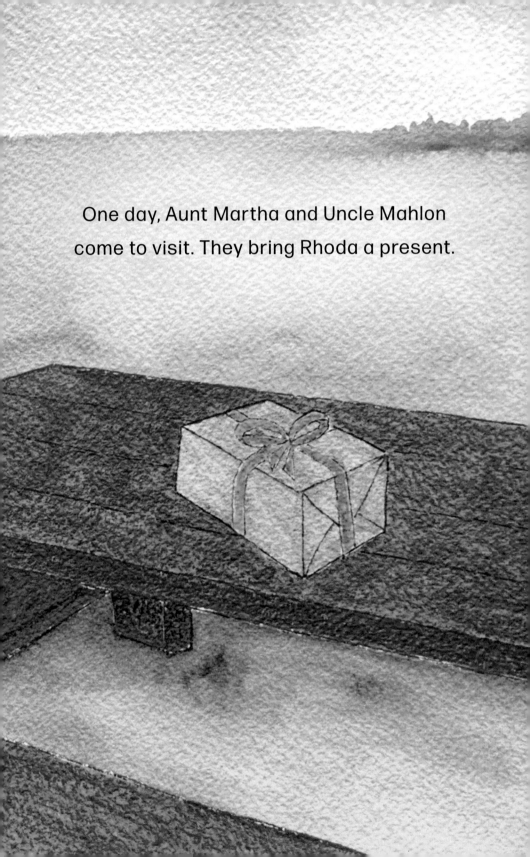

Mother opens the package and looks inside.
She smiles. She takes the present inside to
Rhoda. Rhoda's eyes are happy and bright.

"What is it?" Violet asks.

"Pop beads!" Rhoda exclaims.

The pop beads shine with a soft red color. Rhoda touches the small, smooth beads. She pours the beads onto the quilt that covers her bed.

Violet climbs up on her sister's bed. She touches the beads. They feel smooth. Together they play with Rhoda's red pop beads.

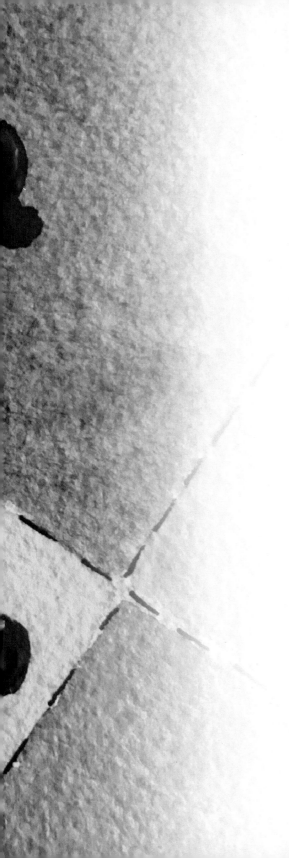

They push the
beads together.

Snap!

Then, they pull
them apart.

Pop!

They make a necklace for Rhoda.
They make a bracelet for Violet.

Mother comes into the bedroom. "Rhoda, the necklace is gorgeous!" she said. "Violet, the bracelet is ravishing!" The two girls giggle.

Soon Rhoda becomes sleepy and closes her eyes for a nap. Violet wants to play with the beads in their large kitchen while Rhoda sleeps. But Mother says, "Those are your sister's beads. When you want to play with the beads, you must wait until Rhoda is awake. Then you may sit on the bed and play with your sister."

Outside the sun shines. The red roses bloom. Dinger, the neighbor's dog, waits in the soft green grass. But Violet and Rhoda do not go outside.

Violet waits for Rhoda to wake up so they can play with the red pop beads.

The next morning,
Rhoda is still very sick.
Mother looks worried.
The doctor looks worried.

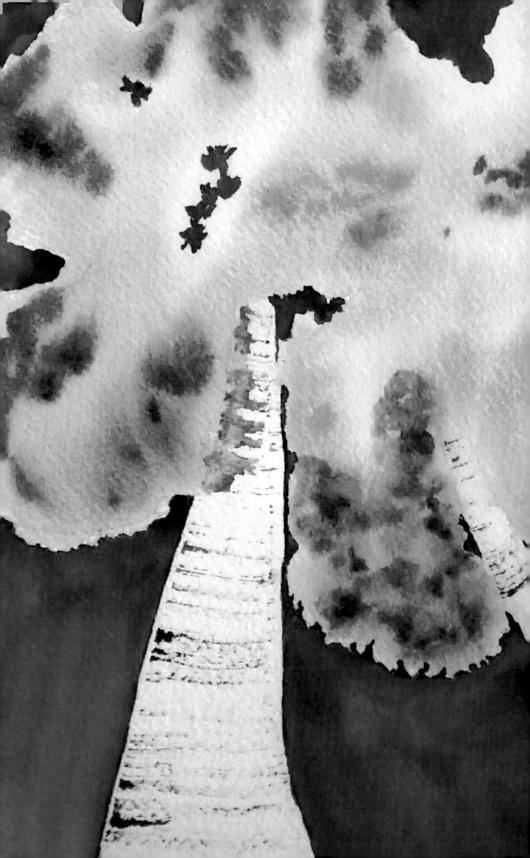

That night, Mother sits in her rocking chair and holds Rhoda in her arms. "Shush, little girl, and go to sleep," Mother whispers.

The next night, Violet and Rhoda's parents take Rhoda to the hospital. They are gone for a long time. When they come home the next morning, Rhoda is not with them. Mother holds Violet on her lap. Father's face looks very sad. Mother and Father tell Violet, "Your sister is in heaven." Violet wonders, "What does this mean?"

Every day Violet wants to play with her sister and the red pop beads, but Rhoda does not come home. Violet looks and looks for the red pop beads. The red pop beads are nowhere to be found.

Outside the sun still shines. The red roses still bloom. Dinger, the neighbor's dog, still waits, lying in the soft green grass. But . . . Violet does not want to go outside.

She says to Mother, "I want to play with my sister! Where is she? I want to play with the red pop beads. Where are they? Please, I want to play with the red pop beads. When is Rhoda coming back home?" Mother says, "Rhoda is in heaven. You cannot play with the red pop beads. They are put away." Rhoda does not come home that day.

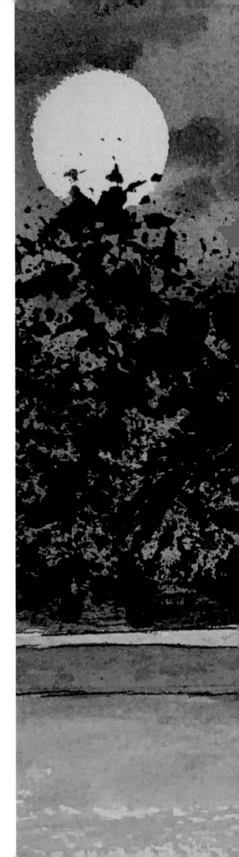

The next day and the next day,
Violet stays inside the house.
She asks her mother when Rhoda
is coming home and when can
she play with the red pop beads.
Every day her mother tells her
that Rhoda is in heaven, and the
beads are put away.

Violet is very sad. Rhoda does not come home again. Violet cannot play with her sister. Violet cannot find the red pop beads.

Many years pass. Violet has stopped asking her mother when Rhoda is coming home. But sometimes she still asks, "Mom, where are the red pop beads? I want to see them."

Mother says, "I don't know. I don't remember. Let's look for them." Violet follows Mother to the closet where Rhoda's toys are put away. Mother and Violet search through Rhoda's toys, but they cannot find the red pop beads.

One day, when Violet's entire family is together, her younger sister, Lois, says, "I want to know more about my sister who went to heaven a long time ago."

She takes Rhoda's toys from the closet and walks outside. She puts them on a table where everyone can see them. The sun shines. The red roses bloom. Violet is outside with her family.

Violet stands beside Lois looking at the toys. Lois exclaims, "Look at Rhoda's little blue purse!" Lois opens the purse. Violet looks inside. The red pop beads! Violet's eyes open wide!

Lois pours out the red pop beads on the table. The pop beads shine with a soft red color. Lois and Violet touch the small, smooth beads.

Violet pushes the beads together.

Snap!

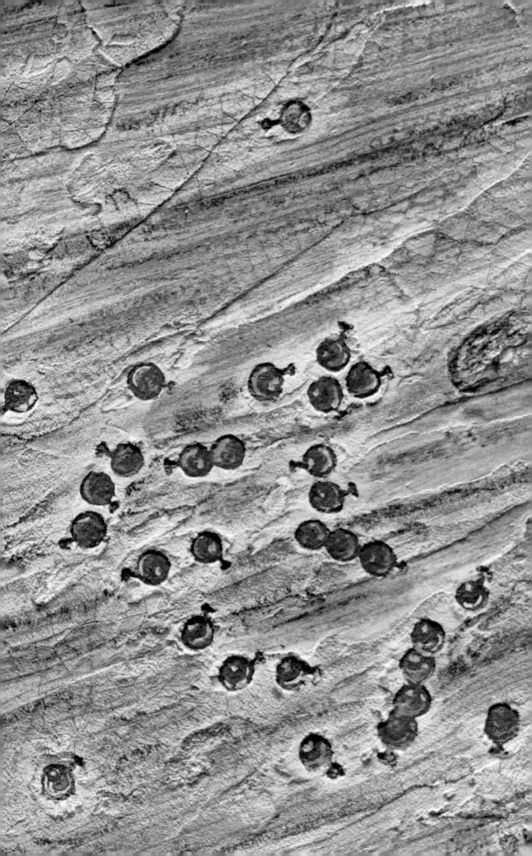

She pulls them apart. **Pop!**